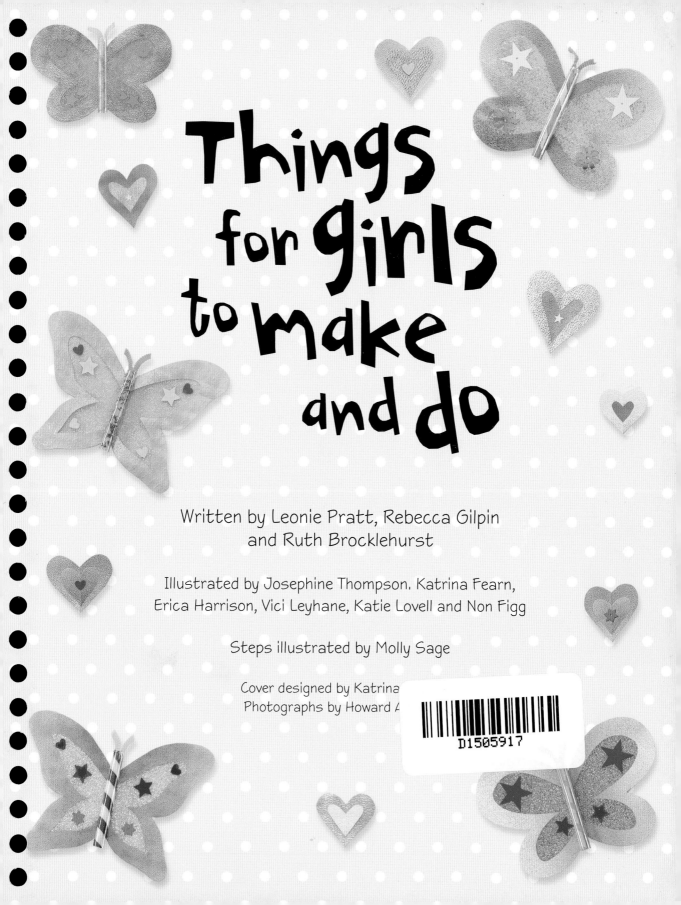

Things for girls to make and do

Written by Leonie Pratt, Rebecca Gilpin
and Ruth Brocklehurst

Illustrated by Josephine Thompson, Katrina Fearn,
Erica Harrison, Vici Leyhane, Katie Lovell and Non Figg

Steps illustrated by Molly Sage

Cover designed by Katrina
Photographs by Howard A

D1505917

Contents

Fairy puppets

This side of the wing needs to be on the fold.

1. Fold a piece of thick paper in half. Draw a wing shape on it, like this. Then, keeping the paper folded, cut out the shape.

2. Open out the wings and flatten them. Then, cut a shape for the fairy's body and arms from a piece of bright paper.

3. Cut a paper circle for the fairy's head and a shape for the hair. Then, glue the hair onto the head and draw a face.

To make your puppets look different, try giving them different dresses and hair.

4. Cut out hands from paper and glue them onto the back of the fairy's arms. Then, glue the head onto the body.

Use pens and stickers to decorate the fairy.

5. Glue the body onto the wings, then decorate the fairy. Turn the fairy over and tape a straw onto the back of the body.

Make a wand from thick paper and decorate the fairy queen with sequins or stickers.

Fairy queen

Draw a face.

1. Cut a pair of wings from thick paper and lay them on another piece of paper. Draw bigger wings around them, like this.

2. Cut out the wings and glue the smaller wings onto them. Then, cut a long dress, a head, hair and hands from paper.

3. Glue all the pieces onto the wings. Then, cut a crown from shiny paper and glue it on. Tape a straw onto the back.

Sparkly ice creams

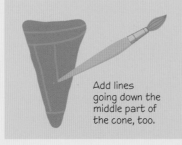

Add lines going down the middle part of the cone, too.

1. Mix brown and yellow paint with white paint to make pale brown. Paint an upside-down triangle for an ice-cream cone.

2. While the paint is still wet, use the other end of the paintbrush to drag two lines across the top of the cone, and one across the bottom.

3. Mix white glue into some pale green paint to make the paint extra thick. Paint a circle on top of the cone for a scoop of ice cream.

Use the ideas on these pages to paint lots of different kinds of ice creams.

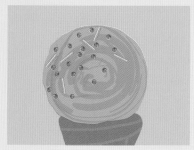  

Try not to sprinkle any glitter on the cone.

4. Sprinkle a few tiny beads onto the ice cream while the paint is still wet, to look like sugar sprinkles. The beads will stick to the wet paint.

5. To make the ice cream look slightly frosted, sprinkle a thin layer of pale glitter all over it. Gently shake off any excess glitter.

6. Paint a dark brown chocolate bar sticking out from the ice cream. Then, use a toothpick to drag wavy lines in the wet paint.

The scoops in this big cone were painted, then swirls of different paints brushed on top.

Tissue paper flowers

Hold all the layers together as you cut.

1. To make the petals, fold a big piece of tissue paper in half. Fold the paper in half twice more, then draw a heart and cut it out.

2. For the stem, gently push a pipe cleaner through one of the petals, near the pointed end. Slide the petal a little way down.

3. Thread the rest of the petals on in the same way. Then, gently spread the petals out around the stem, to make a flower.

4. Holding the petals from underneath, wrap a short piece of sticky tape around them and press it onto the stem, to secure the petals.

The heart should be this way up.

5. For a leaf, fold a piece of tissue paper in half. Draw a heart on it, then cut out the shape, keeping the paper folded.

6. Cut another pipe cleaner in half. Spread glue on one of the leaves, then press the end of the pipe cleaner onto the glue.

To make a bouquet, tie lots of flowers together with a shiny ribbon.

You could use different shades of tissue paper for the flowers.

7. Press the other leaf over the top and leave the glue to dry. Then, gently brush white glue over the top of the leaf.

8. Sprinkle glitter over the wet glue and leave it to dry. Then, lay the leaf stem next to the main stem and twist them together tightly.

Princess in a tower

You only need one half for the roof.

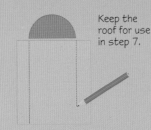

Keep the roof for use in step 7.

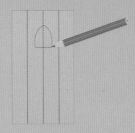

1. To make the roof, draw around a small plate on thick paper. Cut out the circle, fold it in half, then unfold it. Cut along the line.

2. Lay the roof at the top of a piece of thick paper. Draw lines down from each end. Then, cut along the lines to make the tower.

3. Draw a line down the middle of the tower. Then, add lines on either side of it, like this. Draw a window over the middle line, too.

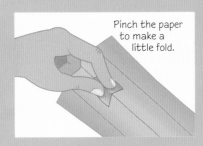

Pinch the paper to make a little fold.

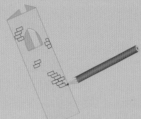

The front of the tower will curve as you overlap the edges.

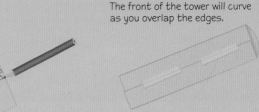

4. Pinch the paper in the middle of the window. Make a cut into the fold, then cut out the window, starting from the cut.

5. Fold the edges back, along the lines on either side of the window. Erase the middle pencil line, then draw bricks on the tower.

6. To make the tower 3-D, turn it over and pull the edges together until they overlap. Then, use sticky tape to secure the edges.

Erase the middle line when the ink is dry.

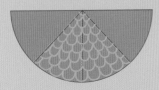

To make trees like these, roll up thin strips of green and pink paper, then glue them onto a circle of green paper.

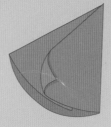

7. With a pencil, draw lines on the roof to divide it into four sections, like this. Use a felt-tip pen to draw tiles on the two middle sections.

8. Fold back the outer sections along the pencil lines. Then, pull the edges together until they overlap and secure them with tape.

The windowsill should be wider than the window.

9. Draw a princess's head and long hair on a piece of paper. Add the top of her body and a windowsill. Then, fill her in using pencils.

10. Cut out the shapes. Glue the windowsill below the window. Then, spread glue around the top of the tower and push the roof on.

You could glue your tower onto a paper background, like this one.

Swish bag

You don't need this part, but you will need the handles.

Don't draw around the handles.

1. Flatten a paper sandwich bag and use a ruler to draw a line across it, like this. Cut along the line, through all the layers of the bag.

2. Cut the handles off the top of the bag. Paint them, and the sides of the bag, red. When the paint is dry, tape the handles on.

3. Lay the bag on a piece of thin red cardboard. Draw around it twice and cut out both rectangles. Glue one to the back of the bag.

The lid of a spice jar is a good size.

4. Draw around the lid of a small jar to make lots of circles on pieces of red, pink and gold cardboard or thick paper. Then, cut them out.

The circles on your bag will swish as you carry it.

You could make a little purse like this to match your bag.

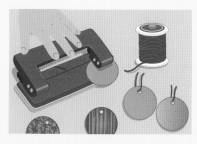

5. Use a hole puncher to make a hole near the edge of each circle. Then, push a short thread through the hole in each circle.

6. With the thread at the top, lay one circle in the bottom corner of the spare red rectangle, like this. Tape the thread in place.

7. Tape more circles all along the bottom of the rectangle, in the same way. They should overlap each other slightly at the sides.

You can decorate your bag with hearts or a bow, too.

8. Tape another row of circles above the first row, so each circle hangs over the one below it. Add more rows to fill the rectangle.

9. Then, glue the decorated rectangle to the front of the bag. For a fur trim, glue cotton balls and sequins along the top of the bag.

Love bugs

1. For a bug's body, cut a piece of kitchen foil that is about the size of this page. Then, crush the foil to make a rounded body.

You need to make three pairs of legs.

2. For the legs, cut a third off three pipe cleaners. Bend the longer pieces into squashed 'M' shapes with feet sticking out, like these.

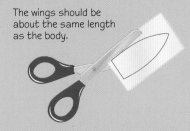

Cut off any foil that you don't need.

3. Tape the legs onto the body. Then, cut a strip of kitchen foil. Lay the foil over the legs and scrunch it tightly between them.

4. Rip lots of small pieces from pink tissue paper. Then, using a paintbrush, brush part of the love bug's body with white glue.

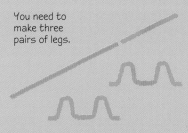

5. Press the pieces of tissue paper onto the wet glue. Then, brush on more glue and press on more paper, until the body is covered.

The wings should be about the same length as the body.

6. For the wings, fold a piece of thick paper in half. Draw a wing shape on it, then cut out the shape, through both layers of paper.

Decorate your bug with sequins and stickers.

Curve the wings like this.

You could cut out leaves for your bug to sit on.

7. Curve the bug's wings a little, using your fingers. Then, for the bug's feelers, cut two thin, pointed strips from thick paper.

Push in the feelers when the glue is still wet.

8. Glue the front ends of the wings onto the body and push the feelers under them. Then, gently curl the pointed ends of the feelers.

9. For eyes, cut circles from paper, then glue smaller circles in the middle. Glue the eyes onto the bug and decorate its wings.

10. Cut a small heart from pink or red paper and write a message on it. Bend the card a little, then slide it under the wings.

Fairy palace

Add extra
decorations to
the palace with
a gold pen.

You could paint some
fairies around the palace.

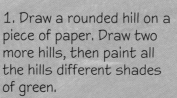

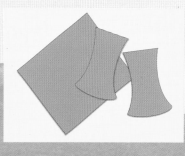

1. Draw a rounded hill on a piece of paper. Draw two more hills, then paint all the hills different shades of green.

2. For the palace, cut a square and two turrets from some paper. Make them small enough to fit on one of the hills.

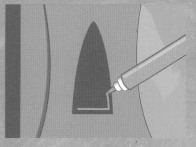

3. Paint a sun and a sky, then glue the palace onto a hill. Then, cut pink paper roofs and glue them onto the palace.

4. Cut windows and doors from paper and glue them onto the palace. Then, draw frames on them with a felt-tip pen.

5. Cut out some small paper hearts and glue one on the top of each roof. Then, paint some trees on the background.

6. Cut out photographs of flowers from old magazines and glue them onto the background. Then, draw stalks and leaves.

Make a jewel for fastening by following steps 6-7 on page 41.

Pretty shell purse

Make the teardrop a little longer than your middle finger.

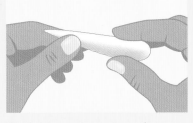

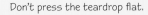

Don't press the teardrop flat.

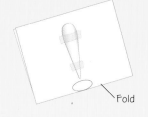

Fold

1. Draw a teardrop shape with long, straight sides on thick paper. Cut it out and draw around it four times. Cut out the shapes.

2. Hold one teardrop like this. Then, push the sides together to make it curved. Make all the teardrops curved in this way.

3. Fold a large piece of thin cardboard in half and draw an oval on the fold. Tape one of the teardrops above the oval, like this.

Fold over any tissue paper that overlaps the edges.

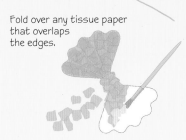

Keep the strip for use in step 8.

4. Tape on the rest of the teardrops and draw a shell shape around them. Then, keeping the cardboard folded, cut out the shell.

5. Rip lots of small pieces of tissue paper. Brush white glue over the shell and press on the paper, but don't squash the teardrops.

6. Lay the shell on a piece of paper. Draw around it and cut out the shape. Then, cut a strip of paper as long as the paper shell.

To make a clasp, tape on a small loop of ribbon in step 7, then glue a jewel on the front.

First fold the strip like this.

Then fold it like this.

7. Turn the cardboard shell over and tape on a piece of ribbon for the handle. Then, glue the paper shell on top, like this.

8. Fold the strip in half along its length. Fold back one edge to meet the fold. Turn the strip over and fold back the other edge.

Shake off any excess glitter before you decorate the purse.

9. Cut the strip in half and glue the pieces in a V-shape on one half of the shell. Trim the ends of the strips to fit the shell.

10. Spread glue over the top layer of the folded strips. Then, fold the other side of the purse on top of the strips.

11. Brush white glue over the bumpy side of the purse and sprinkle glitter over it. Decorate the purse with sequins and beads.

Zigzag card

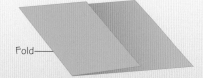

Fold

1. To make the card, fold a long rectangle of thick paper, like this. The front part should be narrower than the back part.

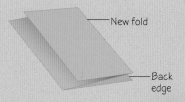

New fold

Back edge

2. Turn the paper over. Then, fold back the right-hand section, so that the new fold lines up with the back edge of the card.

You could decorate a tall card with a big heart and sequins.

Try adding extra sparkle with glitter glue.

Glue hearts along more than one edge of a card.

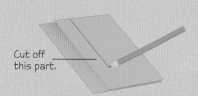

Cut off this part.

3. The front section should be about half of the width of the card. If it's wider, draw a pencil line down the card and cut along it.

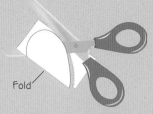

Fold

4. To make the heart decorations, fold a piece of thick paper in half. Draw half a heart against the fold, then cut it out.

5. Open out the heart. Lay it on a piece of pink paper and draw around it. Then, draw around it twice more on other pieces of paper.

You could decorate a card with a flower made from hearts.

The little heart in the middle was brushed with glue and sprinkled with glitter.

This card had different shades of paper glued inside and on the front.

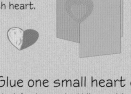

Only glue the left side of each heart.

6. Cut out the hearts. Then, cut out another smaller heart from thick paper. Draw around it three times and cut out the shapes.

7. Glue one small heart onto each big heart. When the glue is dry, glue the big hearts along the edge on the front of the card.

8. Brush lots of dots of white glue around the edges of the big hearts and press on sequins. Then, leave the glue to dry.

Magical wands

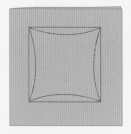

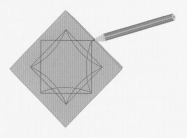

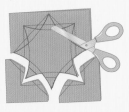

1. Fold a piece of thin cardboard in half and draw a square on it. Then, add curves inside the edges of the square.

2. Turn the cardboard a little. Then, draw another square over the first one, like this. Add curves inside the second square, too.

3. To make a star, draw around the outline of the curves with a red pencil. Cut out the star, through both layers of cardboard.

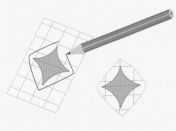

4. Hold the stars together and fold them in half. Draw a curved triangle against the fold and cut it out. Unfold all the shapes.

5. Lay the pieces from the middle of the stars onto some book covering film. Draw around them, leaving a border, then cut them out.

These wands had different shapes drawn in their middles in step 4.

Line up the edges of the shapes.

6. Peel the backing paper off one shape and sprinkle a little glitter over it. Then, peel the paper off the other shape and press it on top.

You could decorate your wand with stickers too.

Hold the ribbon tightly as you tape it.

7. Tape a long piece of gift ribbon onto one end of a straw. Wrap the ribbon around and around, then secure the end with tape.

8. Tape the straw onto the star that has pencil lines on one side of it. Then, tape the sparkly shape over the hole in the star.

Glue sequins on both sides.

9. Tie a piece of gift ribbon onto the straw, below the star. Then, glue the second star on top and decorate the wand with sequins.

Decorated pot

Spotted pot

Put a pretty plant in your pot.

1. Wash a terracotta flower pot thoroughly with water, to remove any soil. Then, leave the pot to dry out completely overnight.

Paint inside the top, too.

2. Paint the outside of the pot with white acrylic paint. Leave the paint to dry, then paint some light purple circles on the pot.

Make the circles different sizes.

3. Paint darker purple and yellow circles in the spaces. Then, paint more circles on top and leave the paint until it is completely dry.

Paint some green leaves next to the flowers.

The spots on the pot above were fingerpainted.

Flowery pot

1. Wash a flower pot, let it dry, then paint it pale pink. Cut some circles and petal shapes from different shades of thin paper.

Use a glue stick.

2. Glue some of the petals onto the pot to make a flower. Then, glue a circle in the middle of the flower and add another flower.

The glue is clear when it dries.

3. Paint a thick layer of white glue all over the outside of the pot, including over the flowers. Leave the glue to dry.

You could decorate a base, too.

Sitting mermaids

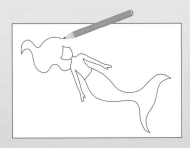

1. Draw a long shape for a mermaid's tail on a piece of thick paper. Draw a body, arms and head, then add her hair.

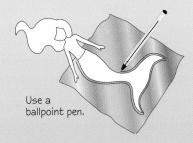

Use a ballpoint pen.

2. Cut out the mermaid. Lay her on the shiny side of some kitchen foil. Then, draw around her tail up to her waist.

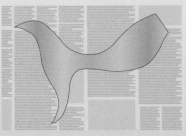

3. Cut out the foil tail, cutting straight across her waist. Lay the tail with the shiny side down on some old newspaper.

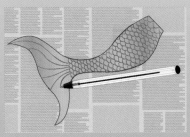

4. With the ballpoint pen, draw rows of scales to where the tail gets thinner. Draw lines on the fin at the end of her tail.

Glue the tail with the shiny side facing up.

5. Paint the mermaid's hair and body. Then, when the paint is dry, add a face and a top. Glue the tail onto the mermaid.

6. Squeeze two blobs of white glue onto an old plate. Add a different shade of food dye or ink to each one and mix it in.

Use a thin paintbrush.

7. Use a paintbrush to dot the different shades onto some of the scales. Then, paint stripes on the end of the tail. Leave it to dry.

Bend the tail into a sitting position.

8. Place your thumb on the mermaid's waist and bend the tail forward. Bend the middle of the tail back over your finger.

Gingerbread house collage

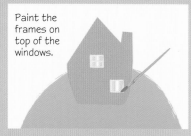

Paint the frames on top of the windows.

1. Paint a hill with a brown house on top. Cut windows from shiny paper and glue them on. Then, paint the frames using thick paint.

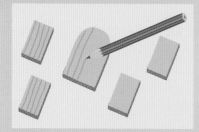

2. Cut out a door and four shutters from an old cardboard box. Paint them, then use a pencil to drag lines in the wet paint.

Glue the shutters beside the windows.

3. Cut strips from the box for the roof and top of the chimney, then paint them. When the paint is dry, glue everything onto the house.

4. For a wrapped chocolate, cut a small square of foil. Roll a ball of tissue paper and put it on the non-shiny side of the foil.

You could use shiny paper or cellophane, too.

5. Fold in two edges of the foil so that they overlap. Then, twist the foil on either side of the ball. Make more chocolates in this way.

Paint the circles really thickly.

6. For chocolates, mix white paint with a little yellow or pink. Mix in some white glue, then paint lots of circles on thick paper.

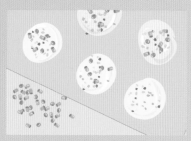

7. While the paint is still wet, sprinkle glitter and tiny beads onto the circles. Cut out the chocolates when the paint is dry.

Sprinkle glitter over the swirls and strawberries.

8. Mix paint and white glue, then paint candy canes, strawberries, chocolate swirls and lollipops. When they are dry, cut them out.

9. Glue chocolates onto the roof and above the door. Then, glue strawberries onto the shutters. Glue the canes and lollipops onto the hill.

This path was
cut from paper,
then decorated
with circles cut
from shiny paper.

These lollipops
have toothpicks
for sticks.

Princess door sign

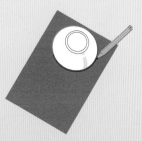  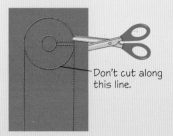

1. Lay a small plate or bowl near the top of a long piece of thin cardboard. Then, draw around the plate or bowl with a pencil.

2. Draw two lines from the circle to the bottom of the cardboard. Lay the lid of a small jar in the middle of the circle and draw around it.

3. Draw two lines from the small circle to the edge of the larger circle, like this. Then, cut out the door sign shape, along the pencil lines.

Don't cut along this line.

Sleeping beauty
do not disturb

You could give your princess a fancy nightdress and a kitten, like this one.

Overlap the pillows as you glue them on.

4. Cut three large pillows from wrapping paper or paper from an old magazine. Then, glue them across the sign, below the round hole.

If the hair is wider than the sign, trim off the edges.

5. Draw a big hairstyle on some magazine paper with hair texture on it and cut it out. Then, glue the hair across the pillows.

Glue the face over the neck and shoulders.

6. Draw a face, neck and shoulders on some paper. Cut them out and glue them to the hair, like this. Then, add a crown, too.

Trim the edges of the blanket to fit the sign.

7. For a blanket, cut a large piece of paper and glue it below the princess. Rip a strip of paper and glue it on top, then trim the edges.

8. Cut out two arms and sleeves and glue them on, like this. Glue on a flower, too. Then, write a message on the top of the sign.

Princess Rose's room

Tissue paper picture

The strips are for the sides of the frame.

Use a glue stick.

1. Cut a rectangle from white tissue paper. Then, cut two thin cardboard strips that are a little longer than the tissue paper.

2. Glue the strips onto the sides of the tissue paper. Then, cut two strips that fit along the top and the bottom. Glue them on.

Hold the folded corner as you cut.

Draw curves like these for rounded petals.

Draw curves like these for pointed petals.

Folded corner

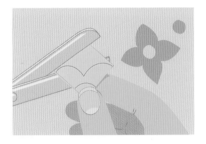

3. For a round flower, fold a square of tissue paper in half and in half again. Draw two curves and cut along them. Open out the flower.

4. Fold two squares of tissue paper in half, twice. Draw a curve on each one for the petals, then add another curve in the corner.

5. Cut along the lines, through all the layers of tissue paper, then open out the flowers. Then, cut out lots more flowers.

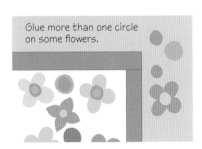

Glue more than one circle on some flowers.

Use a black felt-tip pen.

6. Glue the flowers onto the white tissue paper. Then, cut out little tissue paper circles and glue them in the middle of the flowers.

7. To make leaves, fold a strip of green tissue paper in half, and then in half again. Cut a leaf shape through all the layers of paper.

8. Glue the leaves in the gaps between the flowers. Then, draw outlines, spirals and petals on the flowers and lines on the leaves.

Tape the picture onto a window so that the light shines through it.

Sparkly fairy wings

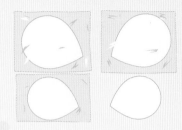

1. Draw two big wing shapes and two smaller ones on paper. Then, cut them out and lay plastic food wrap over them.

2. Rip up two shades of tissue paper and overlap the pieces on the plastic. Cover the wing shapes, including their edges.

3. Mix some white glue with water to make it runny. Then, paint the glue all over the top of the pieces of tissue paper.

4. Press on another layer of tissue paper and paint it with glue. Then, add about five more layers of tissue paper and glue.

Put the wings on your back, then tie the ribbons at the front.

Press on shiny stickers to make the wings even more sparkly.

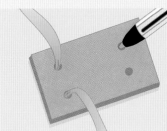

5. Sprinkle the top layer of glue with glitter. When it is dry, paint another layer of glue over the glitter. Leave the glue to dry.

6. Peel the wings off the food wrap. Lay the paper wings on top, then draw around them and cut out the shapes.

7. Glue the wings together, like this. Then, while the glue is drying, cut a rectangle from a piece of thick cardboard.

8. Using a ballpoint pen, carefully make four holes in the rectangle. Then, thread two long pieces of ribbon through the holes.

Leave long ends on the ribbons.

9. Glue the rectangle onto the back of the wings, with the ends of the ribbons sticking out. Then, let the glue dry.

Twinkling twirlers

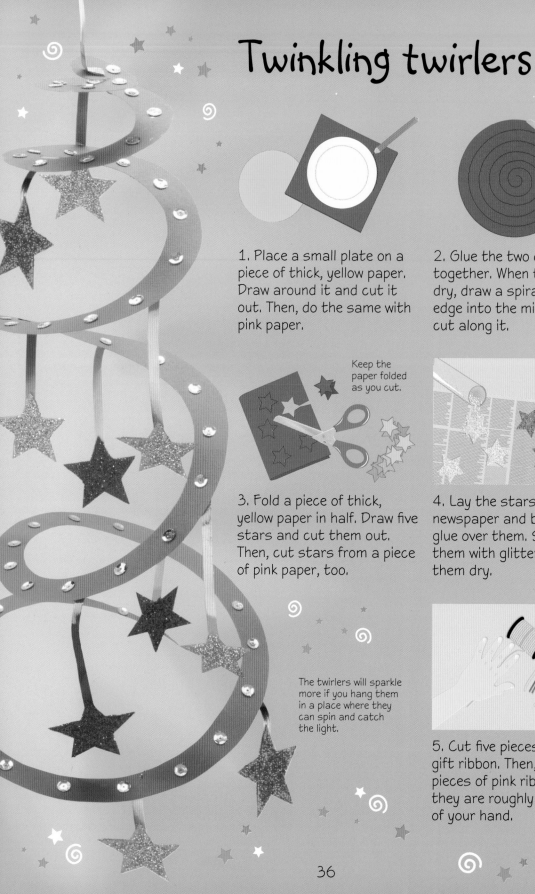

1. Place a small plate on a piece of thick, yellow paper. Draw around it and cut it out. Then, do the same with pink paper.

2. Glue the two circles together. When the glue is dry, draw a spiral from the edge into the middle and cut along it.

Keep the paper folded as you cut.

3. Fold a piece of thick, yellow paper in half. Draw five stars and cut them out. Then, cut stars from a piece of pink paper, too.

4. Lay the stars on some newspaper and brush white glue over them. Sprinkle them with glitter and let them dry.

The twirlers will sparkle more if you hang them in a place where they can spin and catch the light.

5. Cut five pieces of gold gift ribbon. Then, cut five pieces of pink ribbon that they are roughly the length of your hand.

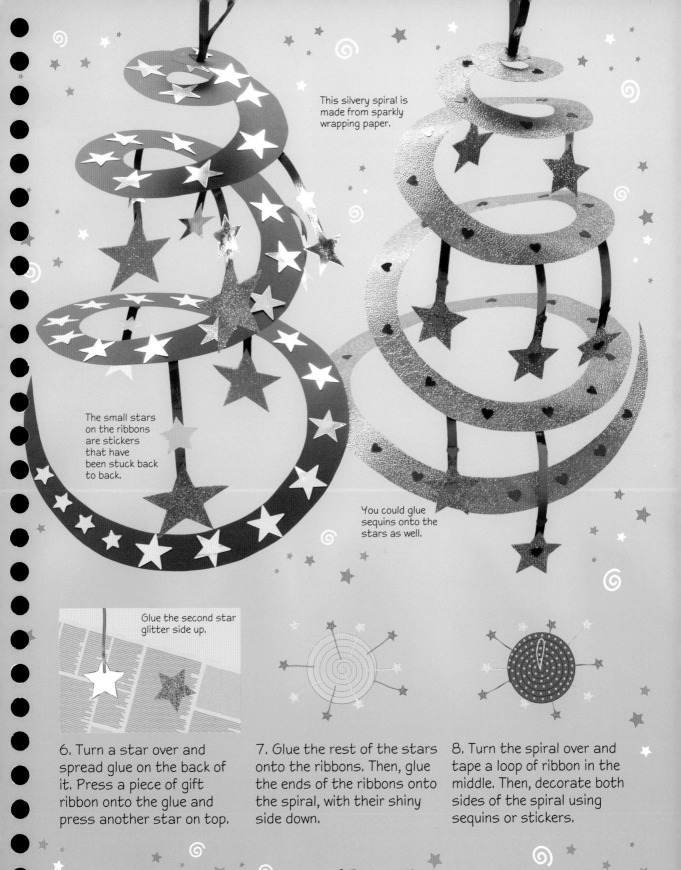

This silvery spiral is made from sparkly wrapping paper.

The small stars on the ribbons are stickers that have been stuck back to back.

You could glue sequins onto the stars as well.

Glue the second star glitter side up.

6. Turn a star over and spread glue on the back of it. Press a piece of gift ribbon onto the glue and press another star on top.

7. Glue the rest of the stars onto the ribbons. Then, glue the ends of the ribbons onto the spiral, with their shiny side down.

8. Turn the spiral over and tape a loop of ribbon in the middle. Then, decorate both sides of the spiral using sequins or stickers.

Tissue paper lovebirds

Brush the glue to the edges of the shapes.

1. Rip a shape for a lovebird's body from pink tissue paper. Then, rip two shapes for the wings and one for the tail, too.

2. Gently brush white glue on the back of the body. Press it onto a piece of white paper, then glue on the wings and tail.

You could draw a tree with heart-shaped leaves, for your lovebirds to perch on.

3. Rip another shape for a body and two shapes for wings from blue tissue paper. Glue them onto the paper, too.

4. Rip lots of small pieces from pale and dark pink tissue paper. Glue them in the spaces around the lovebirds, then let them dry.

This will be the beak.

5. Using a black felt-tip pen, draw the lovebirds' bodies. You don't need to follow the edges of the tissue paper too closely.

38

Make a picture with lots of lovebirds flying around.

To make two lovebirds hug, glue the wing of one over the body of the other.

6. Draw a tail at the end of each lovebird's body. Draw the wings, legs and beaks. Add eyes and feathers on their heads.

7. Draw some hearts on the small pieces of pink tissue paper. Then, draw tiny hearts on the lovebirds' bodies, too.

Coral necklace

Overlap the edges of the circles a little.

Leave a gap at the top.

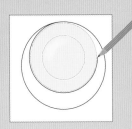

1. Draw around a small plate on thin white cardboard. Lay a saucer at the top of the circle and draw all the way around it.

2. Rip some pink tissue paper into small pieces. Brush white glue on the part between the circles and press on the pieces of paper.

3. When the glue is dry, draw wavy lines along the edges of the two circles, like this. Then, cut out the necklace along these lines.

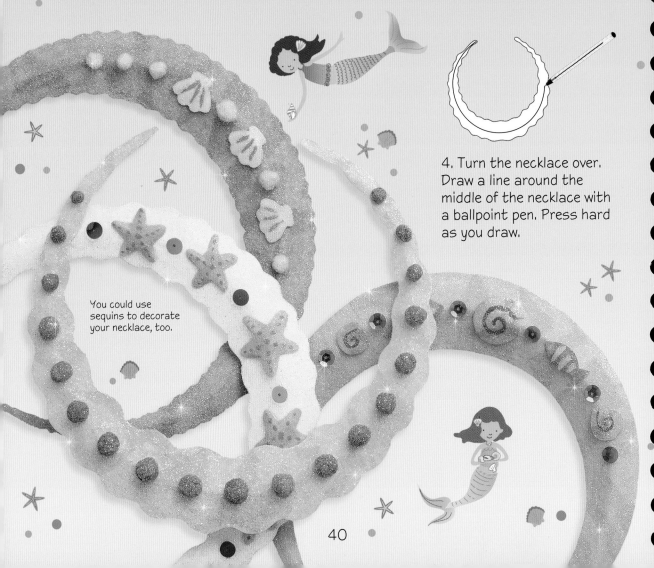

4. Turn the necklace over. Draw a line around the middle of the necklace with a ballpoint pen. Press hard as you draw.

You could use sequins to decorate your necklace, too.

5. Turn the necklace over.
Then, pinch along the
middle line, pushing the
wavy edges together. This
makes the necklace 3-D.

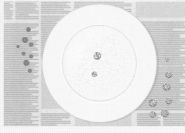

Glue the small
jewels near
the ends.

6. To make a jewel, dip your
fingers into white glue and
roll a small piece of tissue
paper into a ball between
your fingers.

7. Before the glue dries,
sprinkle some glitter onto
an old plate and roll the
jewel in the glitter. Make
jewels of different sizes.

8. Brush white glue over
the necklace and lightly
sprinkle on some glitter.
Then, glue on lots of jewels
to decorate the necklace.

Fluttering fingerbugs

Cut through both layers of paper.

1. Draw a teardrop shape for a bug's body on a piece of thick paper. Make the shape about as long as your middle finger. Then, cut it out.

2. Cut some shiny strips of paper and glue them across the bug's body. Then, cut off the ends where they overlap the edges of the body.

3. Fold another piece of paper in half. Draw two shapes for the wings, making one smaller than the other, then cut them out.

4. Follow step 3 to make four smaller shapes from another piece of paper. Make the shapes small enough to fit inside the wings.

5. Glue a small shape inside each wing. Then, glue the two biggest wings onto the bug's body. Glue the two smaller wings below the big wings.

You could cut out spots or use stickers to decorate your bug's wings.

42

Make your bug flutter by wiggling your finger.

To make a butterfly, cut a shorter body and make the wings bigger and more rounded.

The edges of the strip should overlap a little.

6. Cut two thin strips of paper. Glue them onto the back of the head, then curl the ends between your finger and thumb.

7. Cut a strip of paper long enough to wrap around the your finger. Wrap the strip around the end of your finger to make it curved.

Slide your finger through the finger strap.

8. Fold back the ends of the strip to make two small tabs. Glue the tabs onto the back of the bug's body to make a finger strap.

Dazzling party masks

1. Cut a piece of pink and a piece of blue tissue paper into long strips. The strips should be the width of two of your fingers.

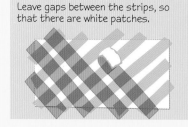

Leave gaps between the strips, so that there are white patches.

2. Glue the blue strips diagonally across a piece of cardboard, leaving gaps between them. Then, glue the pink strips over them.

3. When the glue is dry, turn the cardboard over. Lay a pair of sunglasses on the cardboard, like this, and draw around them.

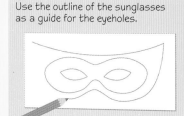

Use the outline of the sunglasses as a guide for the eyeholes.

4. Draw shapes where your eyes will be. Then, draw a mask around the outline of the glasses. Cut out the mask you have drawn.

5. Press the point of a sharp pencil through the eyeholes. Push one scissor blade into the holes. Cut out both of the eyeholes in this way.

6. Turn the mask over. Draw lines of glitter glue along all the edges of the tissue paper strips. Leave the glitter glue to dry.

Don't cover the bumpy part.

Tape across the bumpy part of the straw to make it stronger.

7. Cut a strip of pink tissue paper or shiny paper, wide enough to wrap around a drinking straw. Lay it flat and cover it with glue.

8. Lay the long end of a bendable drinking straw along the edge of the tissue paper. Then, roll the straw tightly in the paper.

9. Cut any extra tissue paper off the end of the straw. Bend the straw, then tape the short part to the back of your mask.

To make a pink and blue mask like this one, rip up the tissue paper and glue it so that it overlaps.

This cat mask has pipe cleaners taped on the back for whiskers.

Make feelers for a butterfly mask by cutting a pipe cleaner in half, and taping both halves on the back.

Princess sash

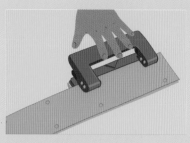

1. Cut a band of thin cardboard long enough to fit around your waist. Then, use a hole puncher to make holes along the long edges.

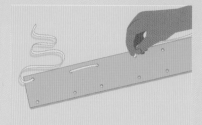

2. Cut two pieces of ribbon, twice as long as the sash. Thread one ribbon in and out of the holes along the top of the sash, like this.

Pull the ribbons so they dangle from both ends of the sash.

3. Thread the other ribbon through the holes along the bottom of the sash. Then, tape the ribbons at both ends, like this.

4. Draw lots of flowers, circles and tiny hearts on some different patterned wrapping papers. Then, cut them out.

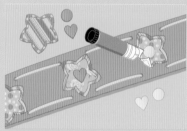

5. Turn the sash over, so the tape is on the back. Then, glue the flowers, circles and hearts on the sash to decorate it.

6. To make the rosette, cut out a large flower from wrapping paper. Curl the edges of the petals by rolling each one around a pencil.

7. Cut two slightly smaller flowers, from different patterned papers. Make one smaller than the other. Curl their petals, too.

8. Glue the three flowers on top of each other in order of size, like this. Use a ballpoint pen to make two holes in the middle of them.

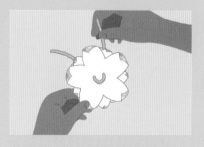

9. Thread a pipe cleaner through one of the holes. Turn the rosette over, bend the pipe cleaner and thread it through the other hole.

You can decorate your sash and rosette with sequins, beads and stickers, too.

10. Twist the ends of the pipe cleaner into spirals. Then, cut out a large green leaf and tape it to the back of the rosette.

11. Glue the rosette near one end of the sash and leave the glue to dry. Then, tie the sash around your waist with the rosette to one side.

47

Pretty heart bag

1. Fold a piece of paper in half and draw half a large heart against the fold. Then, holding the layers together, cut out the shape.

2. Unfold the heart and flatten it, then lay it on some thick paper. Draw around it twice. Then, cut out the hearts.

3. Fold the heart that you drew around in half again. Then, draw a second smaller half heart inside and cut along the line.

Lay the hearts on a newspaper.

The glue helps to keep the hearts together.

4. Open out the small heart that you have just cut out. Lay it on some paper. Draw around it twice, then cut out the hearts.

5. Brush white glue over the two smaller hearts. Sprinkle glitter over them, then glue on some sequins. Leave them to dry.

6. Glue the smaller hearts onto the big ones. Then, dab glue on the point of one of the big hearts and press the other one on top.

To add a spangly trim to your bag, glue sequins around the edge, like this.

7. Using one side of a hole puncher, make holes along both sides of the heart, but don't make holes all the way to the top.

8. Cut a very long piece of thin ribbon. Then, starting at the middle, thread the ribbon through the holes in the heart.

For a gift, fill a bag with chocolates or love tokens (see pages 74-75).

9. Cut two large circles from tissue paper. Fold them in half and push them into the bag. Then, tie the ribbon in a bow.

You could use stickers to decorate a bag.

Funky fairies

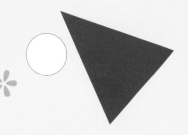

1. Cut out a round head from thin white cardboard. Then, cut a triangle from bright cardboard, for the fairy's body.

2. Cut two paper triangles for hair. Then, cut curves along the bottom edges of the triangles and round off the points at the top.

3. Glue the head onto the body, and glue the hair onto the head, so that the pieces touch at the top. Then, draw a face.

4. Cut out a square of pink net for the fairy's wings. Then, cut a long piece of bright ribbon to hang the fairy from.

5. Scrunch the middle of the netting and tie it with one end of the ribbon. Then, cut two long pieces of ribbon, for legs.

6. Turn the body over, and tape the wings onto it, with the long piece of ribbon pointing up. Then, tape the legs on, too.

You could make
lots of different
fairies.

7. To make the arms, bend the bumpy part of a drinking straw and cut it so that both ends are the same length.

8. Press the bumpy part of the straw onto a piece of poster tack. Then, press it onto the back of the fairy, just above the wings.

9. For feet, thread beads onto the fairy's legs and tie knots below them. Press a sticker on her head and hang her up.

Glittery-winged unicorns

1. Dip your finger in white paint and fingerpaint around and around for a body. Fingerpaint a head and a line for the neck.

2. For the legs, cut a strip of cardboard. Then, dip one of the long sides in the paint and drag it across the paper three times.

3. For a bent leg, dip a small piece of cardboard in the paint and drag two lines. Use a corner of the cardboard to paint the ears.

Try painting the unicorns in lots of different positions.

These unicorns had glitter lightly sprinkled over them while the paint was still wet.

4. Squeeze a line of glitter glue along the unicorn's neck. Then, use a corner of the cardboard to drag curved lines for the mane.

5. Squeeze more lines of glitter glue for the tail and drag them with the cardboard to make them wispy. Then, add a horn.

6. Wait for the glitter glue to dry completely. Then, use a fine black felt-tip pen to draw the unicorn's eye, nostril and mouth.

Dip the tape in the glitter so that one end stays sticky.

7. For the sparkly wings, sprinkle some glitter onto a plate. Cut two pieces of sticky tape and dip each one in the glitter.

8. Press the sticky ends of the tape onto the unicorn's back. Fold up the glittery parts, then cut the corners off so they look like wings.

Striped fish chains

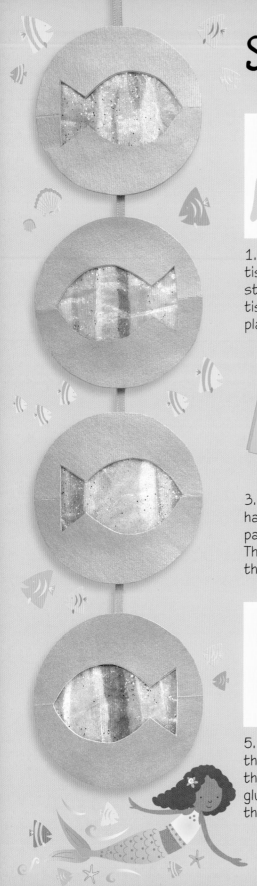

1. Rip different shades of tissue paper into thin strips. Lay a piece of white tissue paper on some plastic foodwrap.

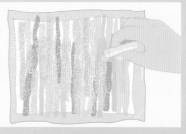

2. Brush white glue over the white tissue paper and press on the strips. Brush on more glue, then sprinkle on glitter.

3. Fold a piece of paper in half. Place a mug on the paper and draw around it. Then, cut out the circle through both layers.

4. Holding the circles together, fold them in half. Draw the shape of half a fish against the fold, then carefully cut it out.

5. Unfold both circles. Peel the striped tissue paper off the plastic foodwrap and glue one of the circles onto the tissue paper.

6. Repeat steps 3-5 three more times. Then, cut out all the circles that have been glued onto the tissue paper.

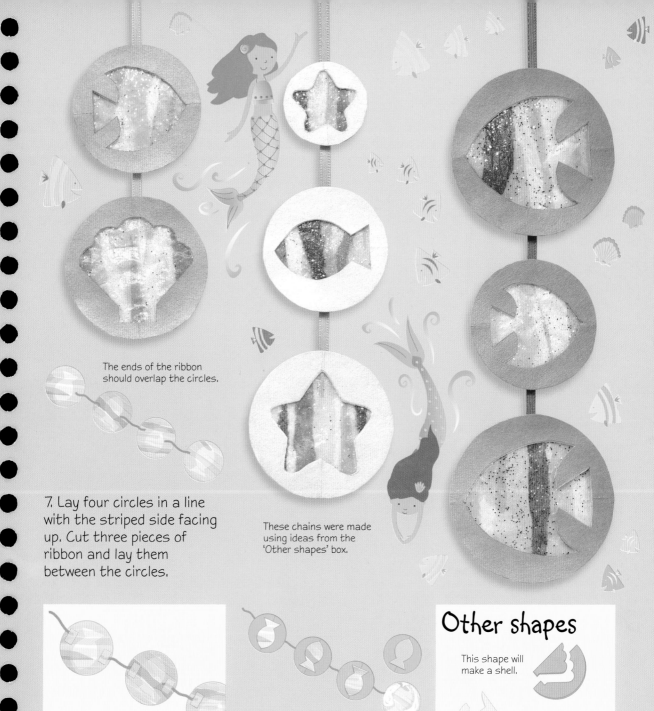

The ends of the ribbon should overlap the circles.

7. Lay four circles in a line with the striped side facing up. Cut three pieces of ribbon and lay them between the circles.

These chains were made using ideas from the 'Other shapes' box.

8. Tape the ribbon onto the circles, like this. Cut another piece of ribbon for hanging and tape it onto the top circle.

9. Glue the other circles on top to hide the ribbon. Glue them so that the edges of the fish and the circles line up.

Other shapes

This shape will make a shell.

This shape will make a starfish.

To make an angel fish, cut out a shape like this.

Flowery bracelet

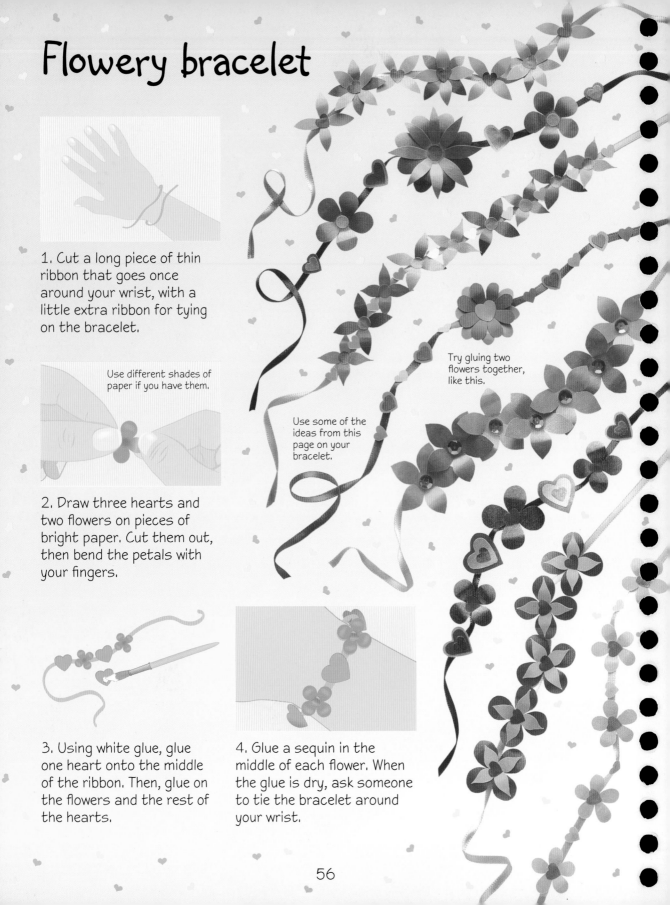

1. Cut a long piece of thin ribbon that goes once around your wrist, with a little extra ribbon for tying on the bracelet.

Use different shades of paper if you have them.

2. Draw three hearts and two flowers on pieces of bright paper. Cut them out, then bend the petals with your fingers.

Try gluing two flowers together, like this.

Use some of the ideas from this page on your bracelet.

3. Using white glue, glue one heart onto the middle of the ribbon. Then, glue on the flowers and the rest of the hearts.

4. Glue a sequin in the middle of each flower. When the glue is dry, ask someone to tie the bracelet around your wrist.

Spiral heart twirlers

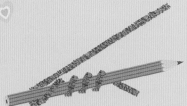

Start winding in the middle.

1. For the twirler, bend a pipe cleaner in half. Lay one half along a pencil, then tightly wind it around and around, like this.

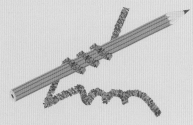

2. Slide the pipe cleaner off the pencil. Then, wind the other half of the pipe cleaner around and around the pencil.

Hold the layers of paper together as you cut.

3. Slide the pipe cleaner off the pencil. Fold a piece of paper in half and draw two hearts on it. Cut out the hearts.

4. Spread glue on a heart. Lay one end of the twirler on it, then press another heart on top. Repeat this at the other end.

Use your twirler to decorate Valentine gifts.

5. For a bag, put a gift in the middle of a square of cellophane. Gather up the edges, then twist a twirler around the bag.

Glittery giftwrap

Keep both pieces of paper.

1. To make a stencil, fold a piece of thick paper in half. Draw half a heart against the fold, then carefully cut along the line.

2. Mix some red paint with white glue on an old plate. Spread the paint on the plate a little with the back of a spoon.

This paper was brushed with glue, then gold glitter was sprinkled over it.

3. Lay the stencil on a large piece of thin paper. Dip the sponge into the red paint, then dab it over the heart until it is filled with paint.

You can print hearts straight onto a gift box.

Sponge red and gold paint over the stencil, then sprinkle glitter all over the heart.

This gift tag was sprinkled with glitter when the paint was still wet.

Don't move the stencil.

4. Before the paint has dried, sprinkle red glitter over the left half of the heart. Press the glitter on with your fingers.

5. Move the stencil and print lots more glittery hearts, all over the paper. Then, leave the paint until it is completely dry.

6. For a tag, lay the heart from step 1 on some folded paper. Sponge paint over the tag, then sprinkle it with glitter.

59

Paper flowers

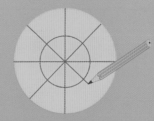

1. Draw around three round objects. Each object should be a different size. Do each one on a different shade of thick paper.

2. Cut out the three circles. Then, lay the middle-sized object in the middle of the biggest circle and draw around it.

3. Draw a straight line across the big circle, then draw another line that crosses the first. Then, draw two more lines across them.

Decorate different jars with different paper shapes.

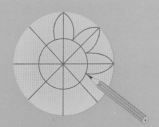

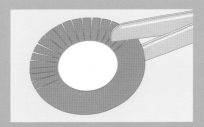

4. Draw petals from the edge of the big circle to the edge of the middle circle, like this. Then, carefully cut around the petals.

5. Glue the small circle onto the middle-sized circle. Make lots of small straight cuts around the edge, as far as the small circle.

6. Glue the two smaller circles onto the big one. Add a stalk by taping one end of a drinking straw to the back of the flower.

A small jar will work best.

7. Press a piece of poster tack onto the other end of the straw and press it firmly into the bottom of a clean glass jar.

This helps the stalk to stand up.

8. Scrunch up pieces of tissue paper and push them into the jar, around the stalk. Cut two paper leaves and glue them onto the stalk.

Shiny picture frame

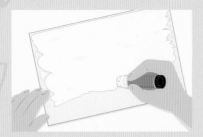

1. Cut a large piece of kitchen foil. Using a glue stick, spread glue all over the non-shiny side, then fold the foil in half.

2. Rub the foil so that the two layers stick together and the surface is smooth. Then, put the folded foil onto an old magazine.

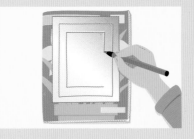

3. Pressing hard with a ballpoint pen, draw a rectangle on the foil, then draw a smaller rectangle inside it, like this.

4. Draw lots of flowers between the lines. Then, cut around the rectangles with scissors, a little way from the outside line.

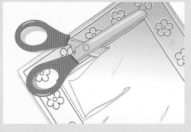

5. Push a ballpoint pen through the foil, to make a hole for your scissors. Then, cut all the way around the inside line, to make a frame.

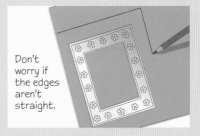

Don't worry if the edges aren't straight.

6. Lay the foil frame onto some thin cardboard and draw a bigger rectangle around it, like this. Then, cut out the shape.

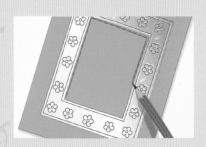

7. Lay the foil frame onto the cardboard again and draw around the hole. Push a pen through the shape you've drawn.

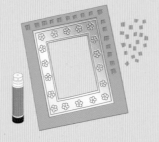

8. Cut out the shape, then glue the foil frame onto the cardboard one. Cut out lots of paper squares and glue them onto the frame.

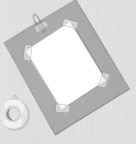

9. Lay the frame on a picture, then turn them both over and tape the picture in place. Tape a loop of string at the top.

You could draw flowers and leaves on foil and cut them out separately.

Make a picture of yourself from paper to go in the frame.

You could make a picture of your pet and put it in the frame.

Spangly butterflies

Fold

1. Cut a piece of shiny wrapping paper and fold it in half. Draw a single butterfly wing against the fold and cut it out.

You don't need this piece.

2. Draw a smaller wing inside the first one, like this. Cut along the line you have drawn, then unfold the butterfly's wings.

Put the wings shiny side down.

3. Cut a piece of book covering film and peel off the backing. Lay it with the sticky side up and press the wings onto it.

4. Press some sequins onto the book film inside the wings. Then, gently sprinkle a little glitter around the sequins.

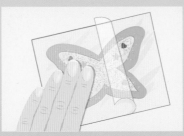

5. Cut another piece of book film and press it over the top of the wings. Smooth the film flat, then cut around the wings.

6. For a body, cut the short end off a drinking straw, above the bumpy part. Cut into the bumpy part to make feelers.

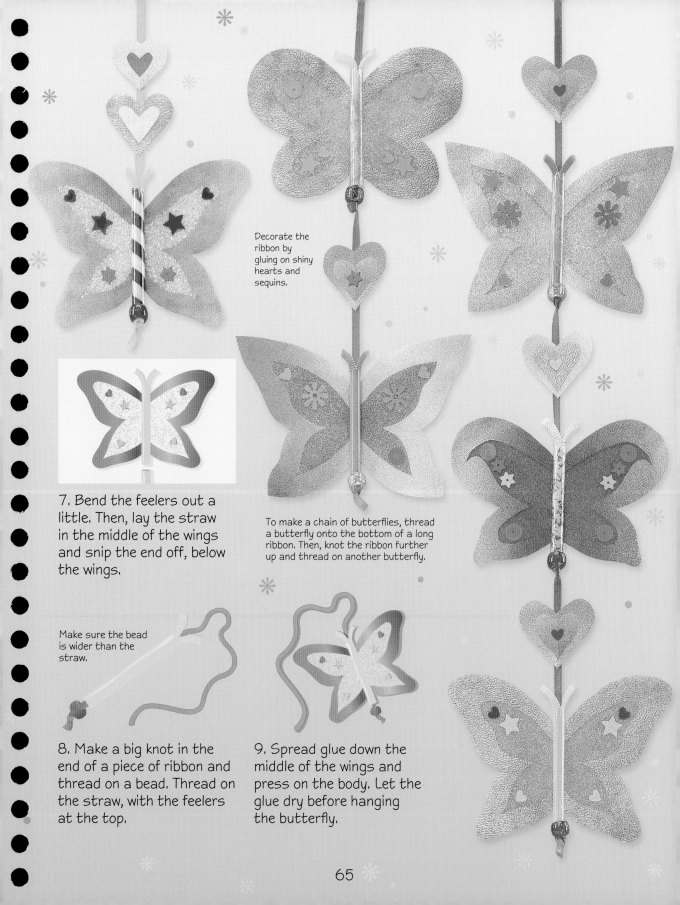

Decorate the ribbon by gluing on shiny hearts and sequins.

7. Bend the feelers out a little. Then, lay the straw in the middle of the wings and snip the end off, below the wings.

To make a chain of butterflies, thread a butterfly onto the bottom of a long ribbon. Then, knot the ribbon further up and thread on another butterfly.

Make sure the bead is wider than the straw.

8. Make a big knot in the end of a piece of ribbon and thread on a bead. Thread on the straw, with the feelers at the top.

9. Spread glue down the middle of the wings and press on the body. Let the glue dry before hanging the butterfly.

Mermaid mirror

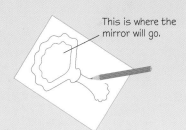

This is where the mirror will go.

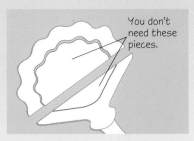

You don't need these pieces.

1. Draw a big shell for the frame on the top half of a piece of cardboard. Then, draw a smaller shell inside it and add a handle.

2. Cut out the frame. To make the back of the mirror, draw around the frame on another piece of cardboard and cut it out.

3. To cut out the smaller shell, cut straight across the frame, like this. Then, cut out the small shell from both pieces.

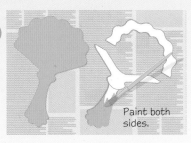

Paint both sides.

4. Put the frame and the back on some newspaper and paint them. Paint around all the edges too, then leave them to dry.

Start here

5. Tape the frame together, and lay it on the non-shiny side of some kitchen foil. Then, draw around the top of the frame.

6. Draw a line across the bottom of the shape. Then, carefully cut out the shell shape a little way inside the outline.

7. Glue the foil onto the back with the shiny side facing up. Spread glue on the frame and press it on top. Leave the glue to dry.

8. Glue sequins over the joins in the frame to hide them. Then, decorate the rest of the frame with more sequins and some beads.

You could draw a fish-shaped mirror, then paint stripes on the frame and add a sequin for an eye.

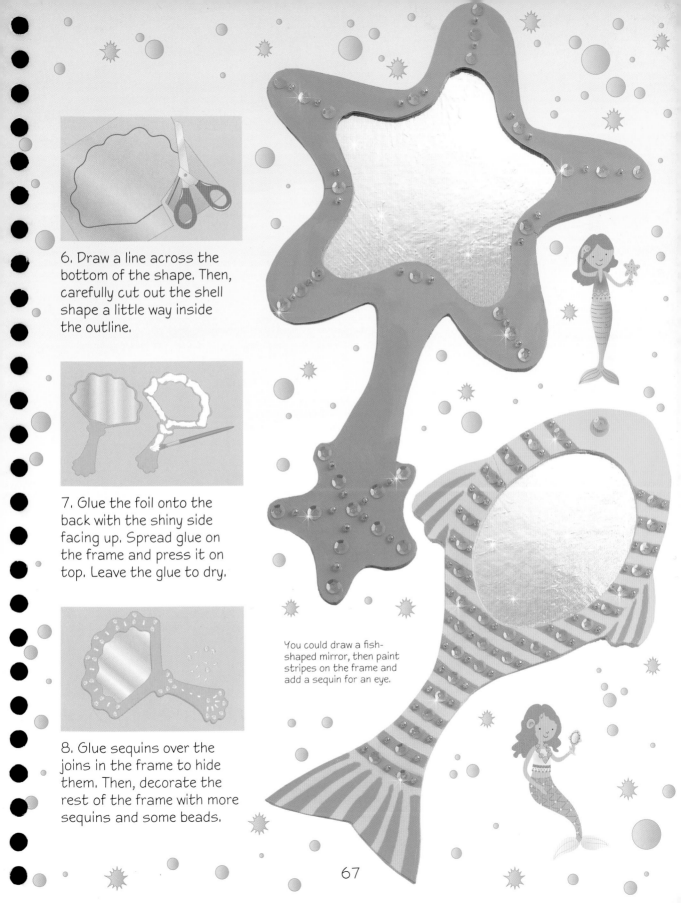

Frosted flowers

1. Fold a piece of tissue paper in half. Place a mug on top and draw around it. Keeping the paper folded, cut out the circle.

2. Lay the circles on a sheet of newspaper. Then, dab white glue around their edges and sprinkle glitter on top.

Make lots of flowers, then twist the stems together to make one plant.

3. When the glue is dry, gently push one end of a sparkly pipe cleaner through the middle of both circles to make a stem.

4. Slide the circles a little way down the stem. Then, firmly pinch the tissue paper and twist it around the stem.

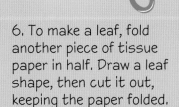

5. Wrap a piece of sticky tape around the tissue paper and stem, to secure them. Push the petals open a little.

6. To make a leaf, fold another piece of tissue paper in half. Draw a leaf shape, then cut it out, keeping the paper folded.

You could use different shades of tissue paper for the flowers.

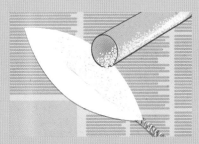

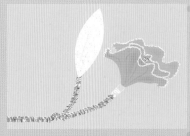

7. Cut another pipe cleaner in half. Spread glue over one of the leaves, then press one end of the pipe cleaner onto the glue.

8. While the glue is still wet, gently press the other leaf on top. Then, spread glue over the leaf and sprinkle it with glitter.

9. When the glue is dry, lay the stem of the leaf next to the flower stem. Tightly twist them together, then bend the leaf out.

Summer basket

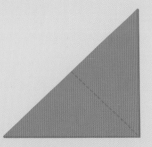

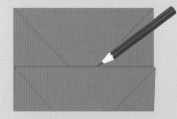

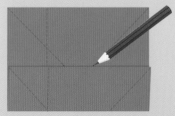

Unfold the paper after you have made the mark.

1. Fold a square of thick paper diagonally, so that the corners meet. Crease the fold, unfold it, then fold it diagonally the other way.

2. Unfold the square. Fold up the bottom edge to overlap the middle slightly. Mark where the edge touches the creases. Unfold the paper.

3. Turn the paper so the next edge is at the bottom, then fold it up so that it touches the mark. Make a mark on the other crease.

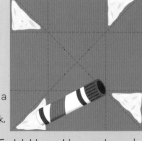

Use a glue stick.

4. Fold the other edges in the same way, turning the paper each time. Then, spread glue in one triangular part of each corner.

Follow the steps on pages 42-43 to make a paper bug.

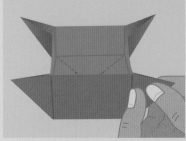

5. Press together the triangular parts of each corner, like this. The sides of the square will stand upright to make a basket.

70

You could make a paper flower and glue it onto the side of your basket.

Try decorating your basket with spots cut from bright paper.

Trim the strip to fit the basket.

6. Turn the basket on its side. Glue one flap onto the top side, then glue the other flap on top of it. Turn the basket onto that side.

7. Glue down the other two triangular flaps. Then, cut a long strip of paper and glue it all the way around the top edge of the basket.

8. Cut a strip of paper. Glue one end inside the basket. Bend the handle over and glue the other end onto the other side.

Pretty princess headdress

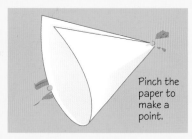

Pinch the paper to make a point.

1. Draw half a circle on a large sheet of thick paper and cut it out. Bend the paper around and pinch the middle of the straight edge.

2. Wrap the curved edge of the semicircle around your head. Ask someone to slide one edge over the other until the cone fits neatly.

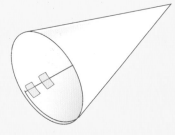

3. While the cone is on your head, tape the edges together. Tape it on the outside, then add pieces of tape on the inside, too.

Overlap the pieces of tissue paper as you glue them on.

4. Rip different shades of tissue paper into small pieces. Brush glue over part of the cone at a time and press the pieces onto it.

5. Cover the whole cone in the same way. Then, cut several long strips of tissue paper or crêpe paper and tape them to the top.

6. Cut out two hearts from bright shiny paper. Then, glue them to the top of the cone, like this, to hide the sticky tape underneath.

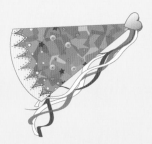

7. Paint a pretty border around the rim of your headdress. Then, decorate the cone with stickers, sequins or paper shapes.

You may need to use hair clips to keep your headdress in place.

Sparkly love tokens

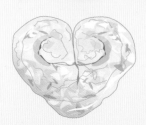

1. Cut a piece of kitchen foil that is about the size of this page. Then, scrunch the foil tightly in the middle, like this.

2. To make one side of the heart, gently scrunch one end of the foil in on itself. Then, bend it around, into the middle of the foil.

3. Scrunch the other end of the foil in the same way. Then, bend the foil around into the middle, to make a heart shape.

Lay the heart on some plastic foodwrap.

4. Press the heart with your hands, to squash the foil into a smooth shape. Make a point at the bottom of the heart.

5. Rip a piece of bright tissue paper into lots of small pieces. Then, brush part of the foil heart with white glue.

Try gluing on sequins or little paper shapes.

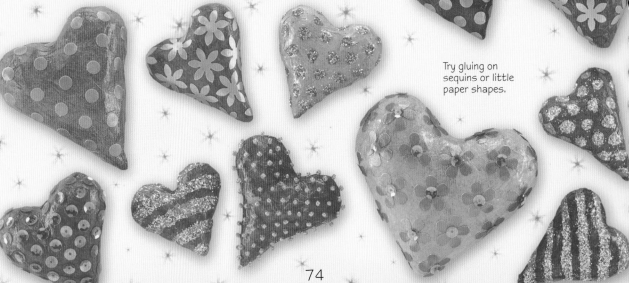

This heart was decorated with tiny beads.

You could fill a heart-shaped bag (see pages 48-49) with these love tokens as a Valentine gift.

6. Press pieces of tissue paper onto the wet glue. Add more glue and press on more pieces of paper, until the heart is covered.

7. Leave the glue until it is completely dry. Then, use a paintbrush to mix some bright paint and white glue together on an old plate.

8. Lay the heart on a newspaper, then paint decorations on it. Sprinkle glitter over the wet paint, and let it dry.

75

Sparkly mermaids

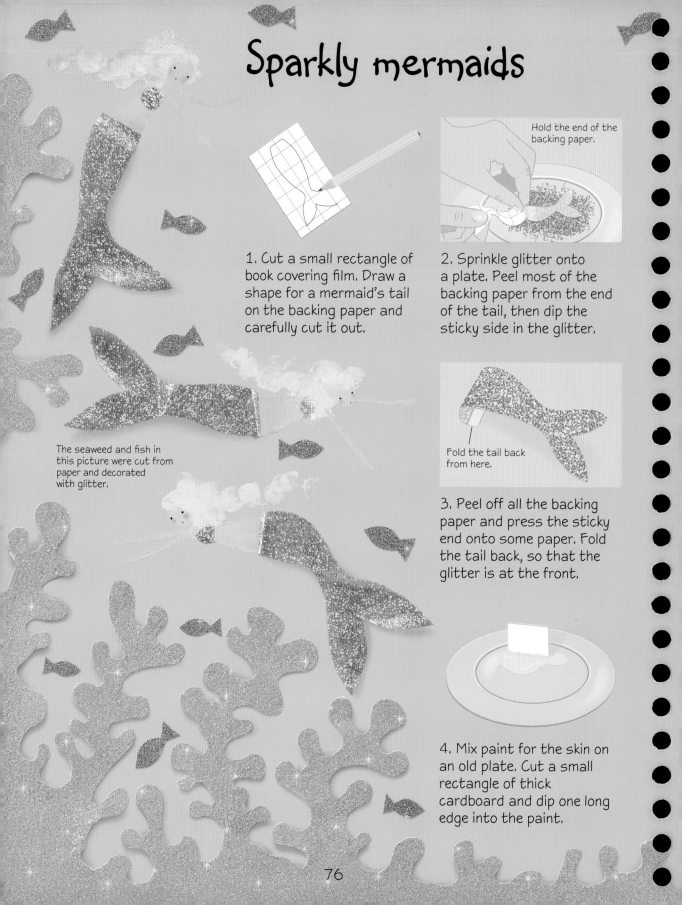

1. Cut a small rectangle of book covering film. Draw a shape for a mermaid's tail on the backing paper and carefully cut it out.

Hold the end of the backing paper.

2. Sprinkle glitter onto a plate. Peel most of the backing paper from the end of the tail, then dip the sticky side in the glitter.

Fold the tail back from here.

3. Peel off all the backing paper and press the sticky end onto some paper. Fold the tail back, so that the glitter is at the front.

The seaweed and fish in this picture were cut from paper and decorated with glitter.

4. Mix paint for the skin on an old plate. Cut a small rectangle of thick cardboard and dip one long edge into the paint.

Twist this end a little as you drag it.

For a curved arm like the one above, bend the cardboard as you print it.

5. Place the edge of the cardboard next to the tail. Then, drag it a little way across the paper for the mermaid's body.

6. Dip the edge of the cardboard in the paint again and print two lines for arms. Fingerprint a small circle for her head.

You'll need to dip your finger in the paint a few times.

Shake off any excess glitter.

7. When the paint is dry, spread some yellow paint onto the plate. Dip your little finger into the paint and fingerprint some hair.

8. Use a felt-tip pen to add a face. Then, brush a band of white glue for a bikini top and sprinkle glitter over it. Leave it to dry.

Lacy fan

The crayon lines are shown here in yellow so that you can see them.

1. Using a white crayon, draw lots of swirly lines on a large piece of white paper. Keep adding the shapes until you have filled the paper.

2. Use a paintbrush to cover the paper with pale, watery paint. While it is wet, paint a wide band of a different shade across the middle.

3. Paint two narrower dark stripes along the top and bottom of the paper. The darker stripes will blur into the pale background.

You could decorate your fan even more with gold or silver pen, or glitter, like the ones shown here.

Be careful not to cut all the way across.

4. When it is dry, fold the left-hand edge of the paper in by the width of two fingers. Turn the paper over and do the same again.

5. Keep folding and turning until the paper is folded. Cut a tiny triangle out of each end. Then, carefully cut triangles along one edge.

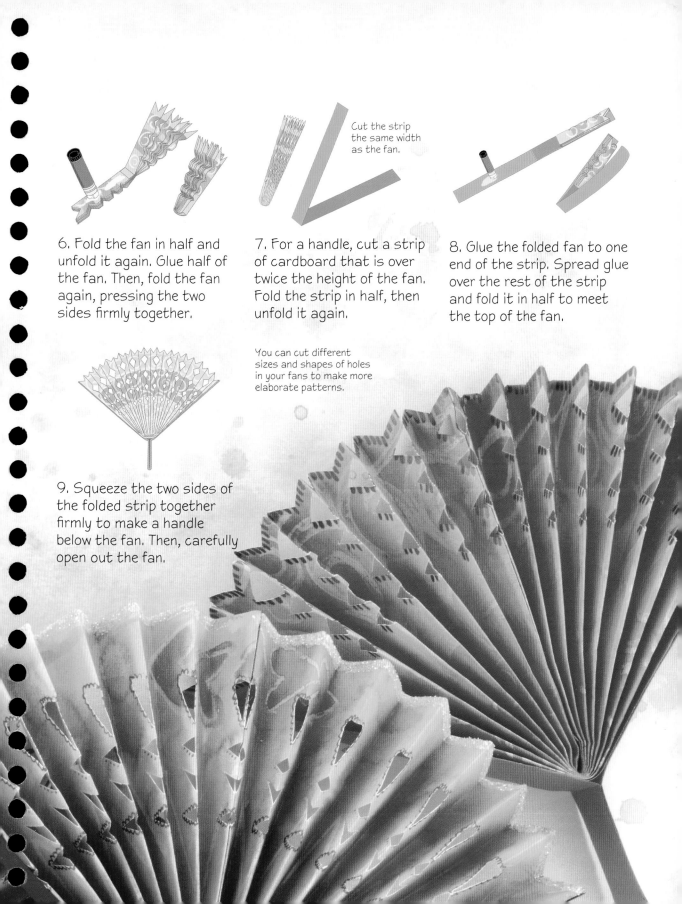

6. Fold the fan in half and unfold it again. Glue half of the fan. Then, fold the fan again, pressing the two sides firmly together.

7. For a handle, cut a strip of cardboard that is over twice the height of the fan. Fold the strip in half, then unfold it again.

Cut the strip the same width as the fan.

8. Glue the folded fan to one end of the strip. Spread glue over the rest of the strip and fold it in half to meet the top of the fan.

You can cut different sizes and shapes of holes in your fans to make more elaborate patterns.

9. Squeeze the two sides of the folded strip together firmly to make a handle below the fan. Then, carefully open out the fan.

Printed collage card

1. To make a card, cut a rectangle from thick paper and fold it in half. Then, cut another rectangle from thick cardboard.

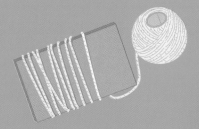

2. Tape the end of some string to the cardboard. Then, wind the string roughly around and around, like this.

3. Wind the string all along the cardboard, then cut it. Tape the end on the same side of the cardboard as the other piece of tape.

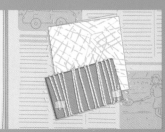

4. Paint the string with yellow paint, so that it is covered. Then, press it onto the folded card, to print yellow lines.

5. Print more lines on the card, adding more paint as you go. Continue until the card is covered in lots of yellow lines, like this.

Try cutting out lots of small flowers in different shades.

You could add some paper leaves and a stalk.

6. Cut a square from yellow paper, smaller than the card. Then, cut an even smaller square from light green paper.

7. Wrap string around another piece of cardboard. Then, print green lines on the green square, as you did before.

8. Glue the yellow and green squares onto the card. Then, cut out a white paper flower and a yellow middle, and glue them on.

Sweetheart chandelier

Save this heart for step 4.

1. Fold a large piece of thin cardboard in half. Draw half a heart against the fold, then draw two more half hearts inside. Cut along all the lines.

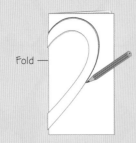

Fold

2. Fold another piece of thin cardboard in half. Lay the largest shape along the fold, like this, and draw around it carefully. Then, cut it out.

3. Follow step 2 to make two more folded hearts, then unfold them all. Then, cut out nine small hearts. Lay them all on newspaper.

Cover the middle heart and a small one with red glitter. Do the rest pink.

4. Unfold the middle heart from step 1. Spread glue on each shape and sprinkle them with glitter. Glitter the back of the small hearts.

5. Cut a piece of silver string about the height of one of the large hearts. Then, cut nine pieces that are about half the length.

6. Glue a small heart onto each short string. Then, tape the strings of two of the pink hearts onto each large heart, like this.

The chandelier will hang from this loop.

7. Glue the bigger red heart to the long string. Fold the string over, to make a loop. Then tape it to the top of one large pink heart.

8. Spread glue on the left-hand half of the heart. Fold another large heart in half, glitter sides in. Then, press one half of it onto the glue.

Make sure the edges and the folds match.

9. Fold the other two large hearts and glue them on in the same way. Then, tape the small red heart to the bottom of the chandelier.

82

When it is hung up, your chandelier will shimmer as it moves.

10. Spread glue on the bare half of the last large heart you glued on. Fold it over and press it onto the right-hand heart.

11. Pick up your chandelier. Then, crease the large folded hearts around the loop and at the bottom, to make them stand out evenly.

Dainty slipper decorations

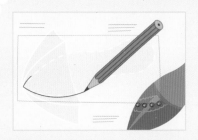

Make sure you press hard.

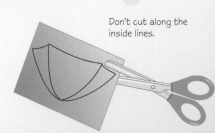
Don't cut along the inside lines.

1. Lay a piece of tracing paper over the template on this page and trace the sole template in pencil. Then, turn the tracing paper over.

2. Lay the tracing paper on a piece of thin cardboard. Draw over the lines to copy them onto the cardboard. Then, cut out the sole.

3. Trace the toe template and copy it onto a piece of thick paper in the same way. Then, cut out the toe shape.

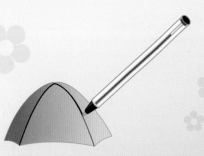

This is the template for the slipper.

The sole template is shown with a dotted line.

4. Using a ballpoint pen, draw along the lines on the toe. Press hard to make a crease. Then, fold the sides up along the creases.

The solid lines show the toe template.

These slippers are for decoration, not for wearing.

5. Cut four slits in both folded sides of the toe to make tiny tabs. Fold the tabs along the creases so that they stand up.

You could decorate the sole of your slipper as well as the toe.

These slippers are shown actual size. You can use them to decorate your room or glue them to cards.

This slipper has a trim made from a cotton ball.

You could use some of the ideas on these slippers to decorate your slipper.

The tabs will overlap each other as you glue them on.

6. Put glue along the front edges of the base of the sole. Then, slide the sole under the right-hand tabs and press them on the glue.

7. With a finger inside the slipper, bend the toe around the sole. Then, press the left-hand tabs firmly onto the glue.

8. Decorate the toe of the slipper with glitter, beads and shiny paper, or draw patterns on it with felt-tip pens or glitter glue.

Flowery boxes

Rub the shapes, to flatten them.

1. Cut lots of shapes from bright shades of paper. Then, brush them with white glue and press them all over a box.

2. Cut lots of pictures of different kinds of flowers from old magazines. Cut as close to the edges of the flowers as you can.

You can use any small box to make a perfect present. It can be used as a trinket box or filled with gifts.

3. Brush some white glue onto the back of one of the paper flowers. Then, stick the flower onto the top of the box.

4. Gently rub the flower, to make it really flat. Then, glue another flower onto the box, a little way from the first one.

5. Glue on lots more flowers. Glue some of them so that they go over the edges of the box, then press them down.

The glue will be clear when it dries.

6. Brush a thick layer of glue over the whole box, including the flowers. Then, leave the glue until it is completely dry.

This was a round cheese box. It was painted and the flowers were stuck on when the paint was dry.

You could decorate the lid of a plain gift box.

For a yummy gift, fill a decorated box with lots of chocolates.

Sparkly tiara

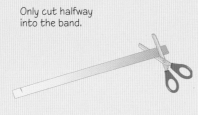

Only cut halfway into the band.

1. Cut a narrow band of thin cardboard that fits once around your head. Then, cut a little off one of the ends.

2. A little way from one end, make a cut going down into the band. Then, make a second cut going up into the other end.

3. Cut six strips of foil that are twice as wide as the band. Then, squeeze and roll the strips to make thin sticks.

You could use shiny cardboard for the band.

You can bend the foil sticks in lots of different ways to make different kinds of tiaras.

88

Try hanging a paper heart from a piece of thread.

The tiara sits on the top of your head. You may need to clip it to your hair.

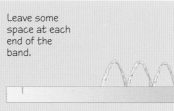

Leave some space at each end of the band.

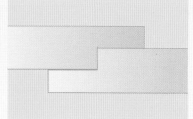

4. Cut each stick in half. Then, bend one piece in half so that it makes an arch. Tape it onto the middle of the band.

5. Bend the rest of the foil sticks and tape five arches on either side of the middle one. Then, turn the tiara over.

6. Decorate the front of the tiara with stickers and sequins. Slot its ends together, so that the ends are pointing inwards.

Dancing princesses

You can paint lots of princesses, with different dresses and hairstyles, to make a large scene.

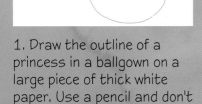

The white crayon lines are shown here in yellow so that you can see them.

The crayon lines stay white when you paint over the ballgown.

1. Draw the outline of a princess in a ballgown on a large piece of thick white paper. Use a pencil and don't press too hard.

2. Use a white wax crayon to draw frills and patterns on the princess's ballgown. Then, draw wavy lines or curls for the hair.

3. Using a thick paintbrush, cover the piece of paper with water. Then, dip the brush in very watery paint and fill in the ballgown.

You could use white wax crayon and more watery paint to add a starry background to your scene.

4. Add blobs or swirls of a different shade of paint to parts of the ballgown. The two shades of paint will mix and blur together.

5. Fill in the hair with watery paint in a different shade. Use a thinner paintbrush to paint her crown, face and arms. Then, add the feet.

6. Leave the paint until it is completely dry. Then, use a sharp pencil to draw around the princess's eyes, nose and mouth again.

Pretty roses loveheart

For a Valentine decoration, glue several lovehearts onto a long ribbon.

Keep the paper folded as you cut.

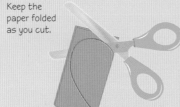

1. Fold a small piece of pink paper in half. Then, draw half a heart against the fold. Cut out the shape, then open out the heart.

2. Cut a rectangle that is about the size of a postcard from thick pink paper. Then, lay a pencil along one of the long edges.

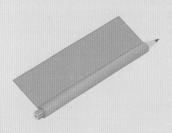

3. Curl the paper tightly around the pencil. Then, roll the pencil up the paper to the top edge. Unroll it and remove the pencil.

Roll the paper on a flat surface.

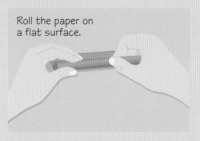

4. Fold in the edge that was curled around the pencil, to make it easier to roll. Then, roll the paper again, as tightly as you can.

The slices get flattened by the scissors.

5. Cut the rolled paper into slices. Then, to make the slices more like round roses, gently squash them a little with your fingers.

Glue the rose near the edge of the heart.

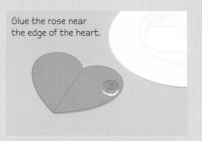

6. Pour some white glue onto an old plate. Dip the bottom of a rose into the glue and then press the rose onto the heart, like this.

The lovehearts look pretty glued onto a card, too.

You could glue a loveheart onto a little gift box.

If you need a few more roses, make another roll of paper.

7. Glue another rose next to the first one. Glue more roses around the edge of the heart, then glue the rest in the middle.

8. To make leaves, tightly fold a small piece of green paper, along its long edge, several times. Then, cut the folded paper into slices.

9. Dip a leaf into the glue and press it into a gap between two roses. Glue on lots more leaves, then leave the glue to dry.

Gift tag ideas

You can make lots of different tags to decorate your gifts with. Here are some of the ideas you could try:

Make a circular tag with a glittery heart in the middle.

To make a glitter bug gift tag, glue some wings onto a tag, then press a foil body on top.

Make tags in shades that match your gift box or wrapping paper.

If you're giving several gifts, you could design different tags using the same materials.

Paint some squares on a tag. When the paint is dry, add stickers or glittery patterns.

Cut out purple flower shapes and glue them onto a sparkly tag.

You can use lots of materials to decorate your gift tags, such as shiny sequins and beads.

Hang the shapes from their loops.

Shimmering shapes

1. Draw a heart on a piece of tissue paper and lay it on some plastic foodwrap. Brush household glue (PVA) over the pencil line.

Brush on more glue if you need to.

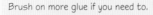

2. Press a length of string onto the glue. At the top of the heart, make a loop with the string and press the end into the glue.

Don't worry if the ends go over the edge.

3. Brush a thin layer of glue inside the heart. Then, cut pieces of thread and press them into the glue, so that they overlap.

4. Brush another layer of glue over the top. Lightly sprinkle glitter over the shape and leave it until the glue has completely dried.

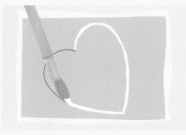

5. Peel the tissue paper off the foodwrap and cut around the heart. Then, glue sequins between the threads to decorate it.

Index

Acknowledgements

Additional design and illustration by Samatha Barrett, Jan McCafferty and Lucy Parris.
Photographic manipulation by Will Dawes, John Russell and Nick Wakeford.